The Birds Help

Sue and Jimmy went to help Mr. Parker in the garden. Soon they saw a little bird not far away.

"Look at the birds coming into the garden," said Jimmy.

"I am happy we put up the bird house," said Sue.

"We want the birds to live here," said Mr. Parker. "They help us in the garden."

"What does a bird do to help us?" asked Sue.

"A bird eats things," said Mr. Parker. "Things we do not want."

Sue and Jimmy went to the _____ . ___house __garden __park

The Parkers put up a bird _____ . ___hill ___house ___candy

They want birds to _____ there . ___ride ___does ___live

Birds _____ things in the garden. ___eat ___put ___best

Purpose: Thinking—details, related ideas.
Directions: Read the title and the story. Then read each sentence below the story and the words at the right. One of the words belongs in the sentence. Draw a line under the right one. The first one is done for you. Do the same with each sentence. Draw a line under the right word.
Use: With pages 6–11, *Around Green Hills.* **New Words:** *garden, far, coming, live, does.*

1

Where is Mrs. Little?

What does Mrs. Little have?

Mrs. Little has a pretty garden.

Mrs. Little is in the house.

Mrs. Little is in the garden.

What does Mr. Little do?

Where does Mr. Little live?

Mr. Little helps in the garden.

Mr. Little lives in a yellow house.

Mrs. Little helps in the garden.

What time of day is it?

Who called to Jack?

Jack called, "Hello!"

It is morning.

Mr. Little called to Jack.

What did Mr. Little have?

What did Jack tell Mr. Little?

Jack said, "Thank you, Mr. Little."

Mr. Little had a letter for Jack.

Mr. Little said, "Good morning!"

B___
b___

F___
f___

R___
r___

W___
w___

L___
l___

T___
t___ 2

far

live

looked

walk

wind

tell

find

far

red

take

look

toy

ride

ran

fun

will

box

best

big

laughed

live

Purpose: Phonics—initial consonant sounds.
Directions: Say the name of each key picture and listen to the first sound of each name. Then study the picture and words in each box. Draw a line under each word that begins with the same sound as the picture.
Use: With pages 6–11, *Around Green Hills*.   **New Words:** None.

The Spring Wind
A Garden Far Away
Spring Work To Do

Polly called to Freddie and Jack,
"See the wind blow the trees.
Spring is coming.
I know spring is coming."

"Look at the apple trees,"
said Freddie.
"They are green and white.
Spring is coming soon."

"The flowers are up," said Jack.
"I see yellow ones here and there.
I can tell spring is coming, too."

"Who said spring is coming?"
called Mr. White.
"Spring is here!
See what I have in this box.
There is work to do."

"Oh, Jack," said Freddie.
"Father has something for Polly
and you and me."

"Thank you, Father," said Jack.
"We will help you.
All of us will work in the garden."

Purpose: Thinking—main idea, relevancy.
Directions: Read the three titles and then read the story. One of the titles goes with the story. Draw a line under the best title.
Use: With pages 12–17, *Around Green Hills*. New Words: *spring, work, blow, flowers.*

4

Freddie <u>works</u> in the garden.   Jack and Polly <u>work</u> there, too.

Mrs. Hill _____ in a green house.   Mrs. Parker _____ in the house.

live   <u>lives</u>   works   work

Freddie _____ up his balloon.   Sue and Polly _____ to school.

blow   blows   walks   walk

The boys _____ a ride.   The girls _____ dolls.

take   takes   make   makes

Purpose: Phonics—verbs with *s*; Thinking—verb usage.
Directions: Study the key pictures and the sentences with them. One sentence uses the word *works*. Find that one. Then read each sentence and the words under it. One of the words belongs in the sentence. Draw a line under the right word.
Use: With pages 12–17, *Around Green Hills*. **New Word:** *his.*

What We See in Spring Time

Polly

Jack

Sue

Jimmy

Polly

Ted

"Spring is coming," said _____. ——Jack——Polly——Pepper
"I saw a blue bird."

"I like spring," said _____. ——Jimmy——Freddie——Ted
"My toy will fly in the wind."

"It is spring time," said _____. ——Jack——Jimmy——Sue
"Here are the toys I play with."

"This is spring time," said _____. ——Sue——Jack——Freddie
"I saw pretty flowers on a tree."

"I know it is spring," said _____. ——Jimmy——Polly——Ted
"I saw a man at work."

"Spring is here," said _____. ——Sue——Ted——Polly
"I saw two girls do this."

Purpose: Comprehension—drawing conclusions.
Directions: Read the title and study the pictures made by different children. Then read each pair of sentences below and look at the chart to find out who said them. Draw a line under the right name.
Use: With pages 12–17, *Around Green Hills.* **New Words:** None.

6

The Party for Dolls

Penny had twin dolls.
One was a boy, and one was a girl.
One morning Penny said,
I will have a party for my dolls.
want Polly and Sue to come, too."

Then Penny called Sue and Polly.
"Will you come to my party?"
she asked.

"Yes, we will," said Sue.

Soon Penny saw the girls.
"Hello, Penny," said Polly.
"Where is Pat?
Will he miss the party?"

"Pat is not here," said Penny.
"This party is for girls and dolls.
Pat does not like dolls.
He went to play with Ted."

The girls had fun at the party.

Who said,

    "I will have a party for my dolls."__Penny__Sue____Polly

    "Yes, we will."_____Sue ____May____Penny

    "Pat does not like dolls."_____Polly__Penny__Pat

Who asked,

    "Will you come to my party?"_____Sue____Pepper__Penny

    "Where is Pat?"_____Polly__May____Sue

    "Will he miss the party?"_____Pat____Polly____Ted

Purpose: Comprehension—identifying speakers.
Directions: Study the pictures. Read the title and the story. Then draw a line under the person who asked each question or said each sentence below the story.
Use: With pages 18–23, *Around Green Hills*. **New Words:** *party, twin, was, Pat.*

7

on   work ———— play ———— off

stop	was ———— go ———— new
old	new ———— far ———— out
little	work ———— off ———— big
work	ran ———— play ———— can
over	under ———— old ———— your
up	after ———— coming ———— down
on	now ———— blow ———— off
in	out ———— jump ———— far
yes	has ———— no ———— does
big	around ———— little ———— get
new	work ———— spring ———— old
here	there ———— put ———— off

Purpose: Comprehension—opposites.
Directions: Study the key pictures and read the words under them. Find the picture with Pat's hat *on*.
Then find the one with his hat *off*.   *On* and *off* are opposite ideas.   Study the words in each row across and
draw a line under the one that is the opposite of the first word.
Use: With pages 18–23, *Around Green Hills*.   **New Word:** *off*.

C __   c __

W__   w__

P __   p __

D __   d __

B __   b __

party

Pat

Penny

coming

candy

coat

best

bird

box

was

work

with

does

duck

did

put

pie

park

Purpose: Phonics—initial consonant letters and sounds.
Directions: Say the name of each key picture and listen to the sound of the first letter. Then say the words and the names of the pictures beside them. Draw a line under the picture beginning with the same sound as the words next to it.
Use: With pages 18–23, *Around Green Hills*. **New Word:** *coat.*

The boys <u>help</u> Mr. Day.

The boys <u>helped</u> Mr. Day all morning

Jimmy went to school.

He _____ for Miss Parks.

work   worked

Mr. White does not take a train.

He likes to _____ to work.

walk   walked

Mrs. Hill had a pie for Pat.

Pat _____ Mrs. Hill for the pie.

thanked   thank

Sue has work to do.

She will _____ Mother make candy

helped   help

Penny saw a pretty May basket.

She _____ up and down.

jump   jumped

Polly saw a little kitten.

She _____ for the mother.

looked   look

Purpose: Phonics—verbs with *ed*.
Directions: Study the key pictures and the sentences with them. One sentence uses the word *helped*. Find that one. Then read the paragraphs below and the words under them. One of the words belongs in the second sentence of each paragraph. Draw a line under the right word.
Use: With pages 24–29, *Around Green Hills*. **New Word:** *basket*.

10

A Surprise Party

Miss Penny Pepper had a party.
Ducks and kittens came.
One brown monkey came, too.

"I have put a surprise
in a basket," said Miss Pepper.
"First you are to find the basket.
Then you may have the surprise."

The ducks looked and looked.
The kittens looked, too.
But it was the monkey
who saw the basket first.

"Good!" laughed Miss Pepper.
"Now here is the surprise."

"Balloons!" said the monkey.
"I like to blow up balloons."

"Please blow up our balloons, too,"
said the ducks and the kittens.
"We can not blow up balloons."

"I will," said the brown monkey.
"I will!"

And he did.

Miss Pepper likes ducks and _____ .	airplanes	kittens	streets
She had a _____ one day.	story	happy	party
She put a _____ into a basket.	shoe	door	surprise
A monkey was first to _____ the basket.	find	first	fly
He had to _____ up all the balloons.	three	blow	blue

Purpose: Comprehension—details.
Directions: Read the title and the story. Then read each sentence below the story and the words at the right. One of the words belongs in the sentence. Draw a line under the right one. Do the same with each sentence. Draw a line under the right word.
Use: With pages 24–29, *Around Green Hills*. **New Words:** *brown, first, our, door.*

11

Do This

Draw a line over the little basket.

Put ✕ on the basket of flowers.

Draw a line under the big basket.

Color the apples in the basket.

Draw a line under the airplane door.

Put ✕ on the door of the school.

Draw a line over the doll house door.

Color the door of the big house.

Draw a line over the first flower.

Put ✕ on the little flower.

Draw a line under the tree with flowers.

Color the flowers in the basket.

Purpose: Comprehension—following directions.
Directions: Read the title. Then read each sentence and do what each one tells you to do.
Use: With pages 24–29, *Around Green Hills.* **New Words:** None.

12

Help for You

Penny put on a new coat.   _1_

The bird house has a new coat
f paint.   _2_

1. A coat

2. A coat of paint

Mr. Little has a letter for Pat. _____

Jimmy will put the letter S
n a box for Sue.   _____

B

1. The letter B

2. A letter

Pepper has paint on his nose. _____

Sue said to him, "Pepper!
Ve do not want to paint you."   _____

1. Green paint

2. See Jack paint.

There is no paint in this can. _____

Freddie can draw a bear
nd color him brown.   _____

1. A can

2. Ted can ride.

Purpose: Comprehension—shifts of meaning.
Directions: Read the first pair of sentences and think of different meanings of the underlined words. Then study the pictures at the right. If the word *coat* in the first sentence means the same as picture 1, write 1 on the line. If it means the same as picture 2, write 2. The first one is done for you. Follow the same directions for the rest of the page.
Use: With pages 30–35, *Around Green Hills*. **New Words:** *paint, nose, him, bear.*

13

Fr___
fr___

Fl___
fl___

Br___
br___

Bl___
bl___

Tw___
tw___ 12

Tr___
tr___

20 blue

twins

flowers

brown

friend

train

twin

brown

blow

Freddie

tree

fly

twin

friend

Purpose: Phonics—initial consonant sounds (blends).
Directions: Say the names of the key pictures. Listen to the first sounds of each name. Say the name of the picture in each box and read the words. Draw a line under the one that begins with the same sound as the picture.
Use: With pages 30–35, *Around Green Hills*. **New Word:** *friend*.

_oat

coat

boy

_ar

far

fly

—y

thing

my

_own

brown

coat

_oat

spring

coat

—oy

brown

toy

_ear

know

bear

_ow

blow

far

_ing

spring

bear

Purpose: Phonics—rhymes.

Directions: Say the name of the picture in the first box and read the words with it. The word *goat* rhymes with *coat*. Draw a line under the word *coat*. Do the same with each box. Say the name of the picture and draw a line under the word that rhymes with it.

Use: With pages 30–35, *Around Green Hills*. **New Words:** None.

Circus Fun

A circus man put on a big hat.
Then he put on a long coat.

All the boys and girls laughed
at this clown.

His coat was too long,
and his hat was too big.

Boys and girls saw a _____ .

basket   brown   <u>clown</u>

They _____ at him.

laughed   worked   called

One little clown put on his hat.
The hat jumped up and down.

"What is in my hat?"
said the clown.

"I will take it off and see."

Out jumped a little brown monkey.

The _____ jumped up and down.

man   coat   hat

A _____ was in the hat.

party   monkey   flower

Joe was a clown in the circus.
He ran out with a bear.

"See me ride this bear,"
he called to the boys and girls.

But the bear looked at Joe
and ran away.

Joe was a _____ in the circus.

bear   clown   blow

The _____ ran away.

bear   door   clown

"See what I have for you,"
called a clown with a big box.

He ran all around the circus
with the box.

Out came big balloons
for all the boys and girls.

This clown had a big _____ .

box   off   basket

He had _____ in the box.

birds   candy   balloons

Purpose: Thinking—details, related ideas.
Directions: Read the title of the page and then the first story.   Below the story are two sentences with missing
    words.   Find the right word below each sentence and draw a line under it.   Do the same with each
    story.
Use: With pages 36–40, *Around Green Hills*.   **New Words:** *circus, long, clown, Joe.*

16

boy   <u>b</u>oy
blow   <u>b</u>low

    Pat is a <u>boy</u>.

far   __ar
fly   ___y

    This circus clown wants to _____.

coat   __oat
clown   ___own

    "I am a _____," said Happy Joe.

bear   __ear
brown   ___own

    This _____ is in a circus.

Purpose: Phonics—initial consonants; Thinking—context and picture clues.
Directions: Say the words *boy* and *blow*. Study the parts of words beside them and write the missing letters. Then read the sentence and write the word that belongs in the sentence. Do the same with the other parts of the page.
Use: With pages 36–40, *Around Green Hills*. **New Words:** None.

garden	friend	circus	girl	coat
his	was	brown	him	has
morning	door	does	first	day
twins	long	clown	Joe	live
work	under	party	fly	our
Joe	Pat	bear	does	please
flower	like	long	live	blow
three	coming	nose	new	his
went	Pat	spring	train	paint
red	far	friend	garden	find
box	best	our	bear	was
spring	story	long	thing	stop
two	coat	off	far	on
twin	street	coming	brown	clown
far	blue	first	circus	friend
friend	want	tree	paint	basket

Purpose: Phonics—word recognition (Test). See the Teacher's Guide—Short Form in this book for the additional use of this page as a test of initial consonant sounds.
Directions: Listen to the word the teacher says. Draw a line under the right one. Do the same for each row.
Use: With pages 36–40, *Around Green Hills*. **Review:** Unit I New Words.

Spring is a time for work.

Spring is a time for play.

Boys and girls like spring time.

They like to _____ and play.

work   was   long

Sue had a little basket.

On the first morning of May

she put flowers into the basket.

Sue had a pretty May _____.

coming   basket   balloon

"Mr. Monkey is my friend,"
said Mr. Duck.

"I will take a basket
of apples to him."

Mr. Duck will take apples

to his _____.

bear   friend   paint

Penny Green put on a new coat.

"Come on," she called to Pat.

"It is time to go to the party.

We want to surprise Jimmy Parker."

The twins will go to a party

for a _____.

boy   girl   door

One day a kitten saw

something little in the garden.

Then she saw it fly away.

"Oh," said the kitten.

"I want to fly away, too!"

The kitten saw a _____.

blow   bird   first

Mr. Jack put on a red hat

with flowers on it.

He put on a long green coat

and big brown shoes.

Then he went to work.

Mr. Jack is a circus _____.

does   nose   clown

Purpose: Comprehension—details (Test).
Directions: Read the first story and the unfinished sentence below it.   Then draw a line under the word that
belongs in the sentence.   Do the same with each story.
Use: With pages 36–40, *Around Green Hills*.   **New Words:** None.

A Long Night
A Good Day for Ducks
Rain, Rain, Go Away

"Oh, Freddie,"
called Mother Duck one morning.
"Come and see the rain.
It rained all night, too."

"I like the rain," said Freddie.
"This is a good day to play."

Freddie Duck ran
to find Candy Kitten.

"Come out, Candy," he called.
"Play in the rain with me."

"No, no, Freddie," said Candy.
"I do not like the rain."

Freddie ran on
to find May Monkey.

"Come out, May," he called.
"Play in the rain with me."

"No, no, Freddie," said May.
"I do not like the rain."

"No one wants to be
in the rain," said Freddie.
"I know what I will do.
I will ask Polly Duck.
She is a duck, too.
She likes to play in the rain."

Purpose: Thinking—main idea, relevancy.
Directions: Read the three titles. Then read the story. One of the titles belongs with the story. Draw a line under the best title.
Use: With pages 42–45, *Around Green Hills*. New Words: *night, rain, be*.

Pat   play   he   do   down

down

clown

brown

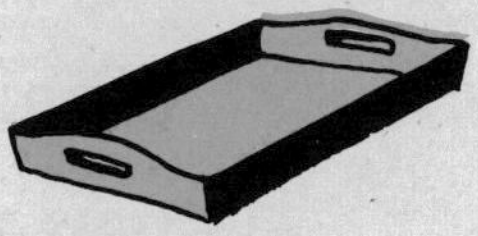

to

do

who

me

we

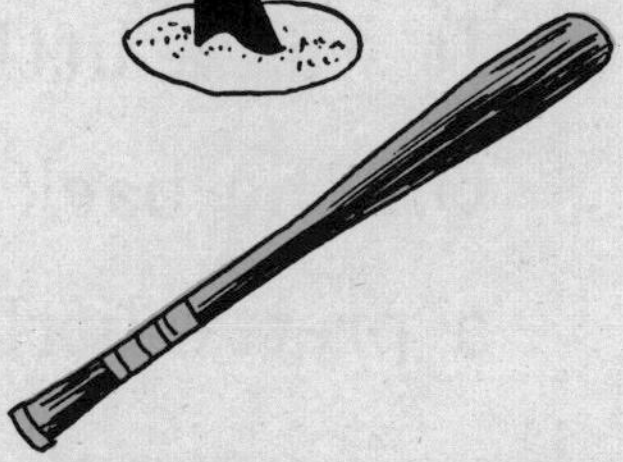

be

at

hat

Pat

play

may

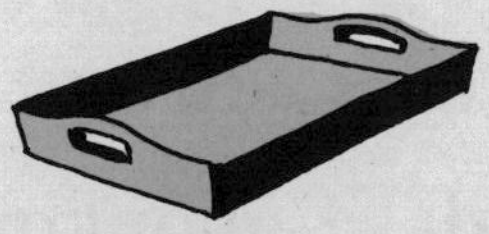

day

he

she

be

Purpose: Phonics—rhymes (vowels and vowel-consonant blends).
Directions: Say the words at the top and listen to the rhyming parts you have studied. They are underlined. Then say the words and the names of the pictures beside them. Draw a line under the picture that rhymes with the words next to it.
Use: With pages 42–45, *Around Green Hills*. **New Words:** None.

A Circus Parade

The boys and girls in Green Hills had a circus parade.

"Our ducks and kittens can be the circus animals," they said. "We will be the circus people."

Jimmy and Pepper were in the parade.
Sue had the little duck.
Polly and Jack had the kitten.
All the boys and girls had animals for the parade.
They were all there but Freddie.

"Where is Freddie?" asked Sue.
Then she saw him.
Sue laughed.
All the boys and girls laughed.

Freddie was coming down the street with his animal.
It was a little toy dog.
On the back of the dog was a pretty little doll.
"Come on, Freddie," Sue called.
"Get into the parade.
You may be first with your dog."

There was to be a circus _____ . _____ school _____ parade _____ party
Boys and girls came with _____ . _____ animals _____ trains _____ balloons
Polly and Jack had a _____ . _____ kitten _____ duck _____ dog
Freddie had a _____ for his animal. _____ monkey _____ dog _____ kitten
His animal was a _____ . _____ flower _____ toy _____ hat

Purpose: Comprehension—details.
Directions: Read the title and the story. Then read each sentence below the story and the words at the right. One of the words belongs in the sentence. Draw a line under the right word.
22
Use: With pages 46–51, *Around Green Hills.* **New Words:** *parade, animals, people, were, dog, back.*

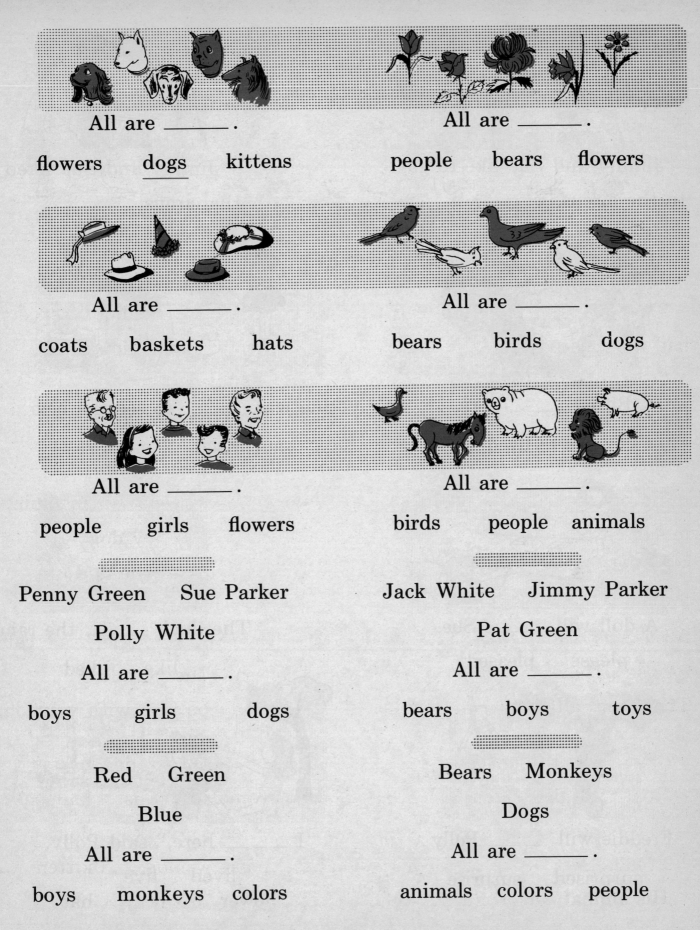

All are _____ .

flowers   <u>dogs</u>   kittens

All are _____ .

people   bears   flowers

All are _____ .

coats   baskets   hats

All are _____ .

bears   birds   dogs

All are _____ .

people   girls   flowers

All are _____ .

birds   people   animals

Penny Green   Sue Parker

Polly White

All are _____ .

boys   girls   dogs

Jack White   Jimmy Parker

Pat Green

All are _____ .

bears   boys   toys

Red   Green

Blue

All are _____ .

boys   monkeys   colors

Bears   Monkeys

Dogs

All are _____ .

animals   colors   people

Purpose: Comprehension—classification.
Directions: Study the first picture and read the unfinished sentence under it. Find the word *dogs* and draw a line under it. All the animals in the picture are *dogs*. Do the same for the rest of the page. Decide what all the pictures or words are and draw a line under the word that belongs in the sentence.
Use: With pages 46–51, *Around Green Hills*. **New Words:** None.

23

Jimmy and Sue like to go to the circus.

Jimmy and Sue liked the circus.

Birds _____ here.

live   lived

Sue was _____ to see the bear.

surprised   surprise

A doll will _____ Sue.

please   pleased

The duck _____ the rain.

like   liked

Freddie will _____ Polly.

surprised   surprise

"I _____ here," said Polly.

lived   live

Purpose: Phonics—verbs with *d*.
Directions: Study the key pictures and sentences with them. One sentence uses the word *liked*. Find that one. Then read each sentence and the words under it. One of the words belongs in the sentence. Draw a line under the right word.

24 **Use:** With pages 46–51, *Around Green Hills*. **New Words:** None.

Three Friends
A Clown and a Bear
The Bear That Ran Away

A clown ran after a little bear.
No one laughed at him.
Then he put the bear on his back.
All the people laughed
to see a bear ride that way.

A Big Paint Box
New Circus Animals
Circus People

Two dogs went for a walk.
A circus man saw the dogs.
"Come with me," the man said.
He gave new coats and hats
to the dogs.
Now they are his circus dogs.

Surprise for a Clown
A Night Parade
A Basket of Fun

Two clowns were in a circus.
They saw a box of candy.
One jumped to get it first.
Away went the box of candy.
Down went the clown on his nose.

A Monkey Hat
Coats for Clowns
The Monkey Who Walked In

The circus man called,
"Come in, one and all!
This way to the circus!"
A little monkey who was out
for a walk saw the man.
Into the circus he went.

Purpose: Comprehension—main ideas.
Directions: Read the three titles and the first story. One of the titles goes with the story. Draw a line under the best title. Do the same for each story. Find the best title.
Use: With pages 52–56, *Around Green Hills*. **New Words:** *that, way, gave.*

25

One Part —— Two Parts

Paint __1__   Painting __2__

Put **1** if there is one part.

Put **2** if there are two parts.

work	_1_	roll	___	blowing	___
working	_2_	rolling	___	blow	___
painting	___	buy	___	raining	___
paint	___	buying	___	rain	___
call	___	laughing	___	jump	___
calling	___	laugh	___	jumping	___
looking	___	play	___	telling	___
look	___	playing	___	tell	___

Purpose: Phonics—verbs with *ing* (hearing the extra syllable).
Directions: Say the word *paint* and then say *painting*. You hear two parts in *painting*. You hear *paint* and the sound of *ing*. Say each pair of words on the page. Follow the directions. If you hear one part, write 1; if you hear two parts, write 2.
Use: With pages 52–56, *Around Green Hills*. **New Words:** *part*, roll, buy.*

26

Penny wants to buy a hat. Penny is buying a hat.

The girls are _____ Mrs. Hill.   The bears _____ over and over.

helping   help   roll   rolling

Polly is _____ up a balloon.   The Parkers are _____ in the garden.

blow   blowing   work   working

Jack and Joe like to _____.   Pat is _____ a new toy.

paint   painting   buy   buying

Purpose: Phonics—verbs with *ing*.
Directions: Study the key pictures and sentences with them. One sentence uses the word *buying*. Find that one. Then read each sentence and the words under it. One of the words belongs in the sentence. Draw a line under the right word.
Use: With pages 52–56, *Around Green Hills*. **New Words:** None.

27

Mr. Surprise

"Come on, Freddie," called Jack. "We are going to school this morning to see Mr. Surprise."

Mr. Surprise did many things. He made a house jump up and down. He made flowers dance in a garden. He made a dog stand on his nose.

The two boys laughed and laughed at Mr. Surprise.

"Now see what I have here," called Mr. Surprise. "Here is my best animal. Here is a horse that can fly!"

Mr. Surprise made the horse fly around and around. There were trees in the way, but the horse went over them. The flying horse did many things for the boys and girls at school.

Yes – No

Freddie and Jack went to school. _____

The boys saw a house jump up and down. _____

A bear rolled over and over. _____

The boys laughed and laughed. _____

Mr. Surprise had many monkeys. _____

The boys saw a horse fly around. _____

Purpose: Comprehension—relevancy.
Directions: Read the title and the story. Then read each sentence below the story. If the sentence tells about the story, write *Yes.* If it does not, write *No.*
28
Use: With pages 57–62, *Around Green Hills.* **New Words:** *many, made, dance, stand, horse, them.*

___n   ___d   ___s   ___t   ___m

9

rain

ran

clown

that

coat

Pat

had

red

did

8

am

them

him

circus

yes

this

brown

twin

garden

Purpose: Phonics—final consonant letters and sounds.
Directions: Say the name of each key picture and listen to the sound of the last letter. Then say the words and the names of the pictures beside them. Draw a line under the picture ending with the same sound as the words next to it.
Use: With pages 57–62, *Around Green Hills.* **New Words:** None.

29

at   it

a   i   _____   _____

_____   _____   _____   6

that	back	him	Pat	twin	his
a	___	___	___	___	___
miss	man	stand	did	big	had
___	___	___	___	___	___

Him, his, this, and **miss** have the letter _____.

Has, hat, that, and **back** have the letter _____.

Purpose: Phonics—short sounds of the vowels *a* and *i*.
Directions: Say the key words at the top and listen to the sound of the first letter. Then say the name of each picture. If you hear the sound of *a* as in *at*, write *a*. If you hear the sound of *i* as in *it*, write *i*. Do the same with each word. Say the word and write the letter which stands for the sound you hear, *a* or *i*. Write the letter that belongs in each sentence at the bottom of the page.
Use: With pages 57–62, *Around Green Hills*. **New Words:** None.

Here is Freddie.

He has his airplane.

Here is Polly.

She has her doll.

Jimmy saw Pepper in the yard.

He called to _____ dog.

he   his   her

Mr. Little saw Miss Parks.

_____ gave a letter to Miss Parks.

She   He   His

Just then, Sue came out.

_____ had on her play shoes.

He   She   Her

The letter was for Miss Parks.

It was from _____ mother.

his   her   she

Sue had something for Pepper.

It was _____ toy.

she   he   his

Mr. Little went to the next house.

He had to be on _____ way.

his   her   he

Purpose: Comprehension—correct usage.
Directions: Study the key pictures and read the sentences with them. Find the words *he* and *his*; *she* and *her*.
See how they are used. Then read each paragraph and the words under it. Draw a line under the word
that belongs in the second sentence of each paragraph.
Use: With pages 63–68, *Around Green Hills*. **New Words:** *her, yard, just, from, next.*

31

see   <u>s</u>ee   [<u>so</u>]

go   g<u>o</u>

The bear is <u>so</u> big that
he can not get into the basket.

no   __o   [_____]

came   c____

You know this boy.
His _____ is Ted.

can   __an   [____]

far   f___

Would you like to take a ride
in this ____ ?

Purpose: Phonics—applying skills to new words from the next story: *name, car.*
Directions: Say the words *see* and *go.*   Study the parts of words beside them and write the missing letters.
Then use all the letters you wrote to make a new word in the box.   Write the new word in the sentence
below.   Do the same with the other two parts of the page.
Use: With pages 63–68, *Around Green Hills.*   **New Words:** *so, would.*

called	danced	rolled	rain	does
from	gave	yard	made	stand
them	her	horse	bear	him
be	many	blow	buy	just
would	them	were	way	one
made	flower	our	old	would
gave	back	basket	yard	paint
gave	good	dog	parade	made
hello	from	horse	morning	so
just	her	made	next	yard
stand	that	animal	clown	stop
our	door	off	dog	long
blow	parade	them	people	be
rain	next	night	first	that
rolled	brown	so	live	from
many	danced	animal	back	basket

Purpose: Phonics—word recognition (Test).
Directions: Listen to the word the teacher says.   Draw a line under the right one.   Do the same for each row.
Use: With pages 63–68, *Around Green Hills*.   **Review:** Unit II New Words.

The Flower Parade

The Little Work Horse

A Horse That Likes to Dance

People Who Dance

The Animal Circus

The Spring Parade

One day a circus horse said,
"There are too many people here.
And there are too many parades."
So away he danced.

Soon the horse saw a man
in a garden.

The man said, "Come in!
I would like you to work for me."

But the horse danced.
He did not want to work.
So he danced on his way.

Soon the horse saw three boys.

"Look at that horse," they said.
"We will ride him."
So up they jumped on the back
of the little circus horse.

But the horse danced.

Off went the boys, one at a time.

Back to the circus danced

the pretty little horse.

There he is to this day.

A bear and a horse were playing
in the yard one spring day.
A monkey came to play with them.

"Hello," the bear said
to the little monkey.
"We are going to have a circus."

"Good," said the monkey.
"I would like to be a clown."

"I will help you," said the horse.
So the monkey went for a ride
on the back of the horse.

The bear had a little box.
"I am next," he said.
Up he jumped on the box.
But the box was too little
for the bear to stand on.
Down he went and over he rolled.

Just then Mother Bear came out.

"Is that a circus?" she asked.

The animals laughed.

"It is our circus," they said.

Purpose: Comprehension—main idea (Test).
Directions: Read the three titles above the story at the left. Then read the story. One of the titles belongs with the story. Draw a line under the best title. Do the same with the story at the right.

34 Use With pages 63-68 *Around Green Hills.* New Words: None

Boy, the Farm Dog

Many animals lived
on the farm next to the road.
One of them was a little dog.
His name was Boy.

One day Boy ran to the road.
There he saw a big brown car
coming down the road.
He saw another and another.

Soon Boy saw a red car stop.
A man jumped out and went up
to the farm house.

"I would like to take
a ride," said the dog.
Into the red car he jumped.
But the car did not go.
It did not go down the road.

"This is no fun," said Boy.
"This car will not take me
for a ride.
I will go back to the farm.
I can have fun there."
And back to the farm he went.

Boy is the name of a _____ . _____ boy ___ car ___ dog

Boy saw _____ cars on the road. _____ many ___ no ___ one

Just one car came to a _____ . _____ road ___ stop ___ story

There was one _____ in the car. _____ name ___ man ___ monkey

Boy did not know _____ to make the car go. ___ now ___ buy ___ how

_____ did not have a ride. _____ Boy ___ Man ___ Joe

Boy liked the _____ best. _____ farm ___ from ___ car

Purpose: Comprehension—drawing conclusions.
Directions: Read the title and the story. Then read each unfinished sentence below the story. Draw a line under the word at the right that belongs in the sentence.
Use: With pages 69–75, *Around Green Hills*. **New Words:** *farm, road, name, car, another, how.*

one car   two cars   three cars

<u>two dogs</u>

one dog

three bears

two bears

two baskets

one basket

two clowns

three clowns

one door

three doors

one animal

three animals

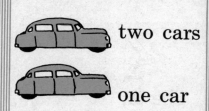

two cars

one car

two flowers

one flower

one coat

three coats

three dolls

one doll

Purpose: Phonics—nouns with *s;* comprehension—definite terms.
Directions: Study the key pictures and words. Then study the pictures in each box and draw a line under the words that tell whether one, two, or three things are shown.
Use: With pages 69–75, *Around Green Hills.* **New Words:** None.

36

Dick has a farm hat.

It is Dick's farm hat.

This horse lives on _____ farm.

Dick   Dick's

Mrs. Hill helps _____.

Penny   Penny's

The Apple Man is _____ father.

Ted   Ted's

Here is _____ toy clown.

Polly   Polly's

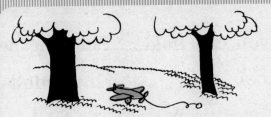

_____ toy is in the yard.

Freddie's   Freddie

_____ has a little car.

Jimmy's   Jimmy

Purpose: Phonics—nouns with 's.

Directions: Study the key picture and read the sentences with it. One of the sentences uses the word *Dick's*. That means something belongs to Dick. Then read each sentence and the words under it. Draw a line under the word that belongs in the sentence.

Use: With pages 69–75, *Around Green Hills.*   **New Word:** *Dick.*

Draw lines under all the things you are to find.

Find the names of girls.   Find the names of boys.   Find the animals.

Polly	Freddie	horse
Jack	Dick	rabbit
Sue	Polly	duck
Penny	Ted	airplane
Dick	Jimmy	hen
May	Sue	car

Find the things to eat.   Find things you can hold.   Find the people.

candy	egg	man
egg	road	coat
box	hat	boy
apple	baby	baby
basket	walk	girl
pie	doll	shoe

Purpose: Comprehension —following directions, indexing.
Directions: Read the directions at the top and follow them.
Use: With pages 76–81, *Around Green Hills.*   **New Words:** *rabbit, hen, hold, egg, baby.*

at   egg

a _____   e _____   _____   _____

_____   _____   _____   _____

yes	Ted	has	had	best	back
e _____	_____	_____	_____	_____	_____
get	ran	red	next	Pat	that
_____	_____	_____	_____	_____	_____

Man, ran, thank, and **stand** have the letter ____.

Then, hen, them, and **went** have the letter ____.

Purpose: Phonics—short sounds of the vowels *a* and *e*.
Directions: Say the key words at the top and listen to the sound of the first letter.   Then say the name of each picture.   If you hear the sound of *a* as in at, write *a*.   If you hear the sound of *e* as in egg, write *e*.   Do the same with each word.   Say the word and write the letter which stands for the sound you hear, *a* or *e*. Write the letter that belongs in each sentence at the bottom of the page.
Use: With pages 76–81, *Around Green Hills*.   **New Words:** None.

39

"I have a dog," said Dick.

"Here is <u>my</u> dog."

"<u>You</u> have a good dog,"
Pat said to Dick.

"I like <u>your</u> dog."

"<u>We</u> will take <u>our</u> rabbit
to Green Hills," said Pat.

"Penny and Pat are going now,"
Dick said.

"<u>They</u> will take <u>their</u> rabbit."

"I am looking for my hat,"
said Penny Green.

"I want _____ farm hat."

our　　　　their　　　　my

"Penny and Pat are coming,"
Dick said to his mother.

"I see _____ car on the road."

their　　　　we　　　　I

"Hello, Mrs. Rabbit,"
said Pat.

"Where are _____ baby rabbits?"

your　　　　they　　　　you

"Hello, Mrs. Hen,"
said Penny.

"Where are _____ eggs?"

their　　　　we　　　　your

"We have a horse," said Dick.

"We named _____ horse Joe."

our　　　　you　　　　your

"Look in that box," said Dick.

"The hens put _____ eggs in there."

their　　　　we　　　　they

Purpose: Comprehension—correct usage.
Directions: Study the key pictures and read the sentences with them. See how each underlined word is used.
　Then read each paragraph and draw a line under the word that belongs in the second sentence.
Use: With pages 76–81, *Around Green Hills.* **New Word:** *their.*

40

Mr. Pepper's Pigs

Many happy little pigs lived on Mr. Pepper's farm.
All they did was eat.

One day a little pig said,
"When is Mr. Pepper coming?
When is he coming to feed us?
I want something to eat."

"I can find something to eat," said another little pig.
"I will go and get it."

The little pig ran up to the fence.
He did not know how to climb.

"Oh me, oh my!" said the pig.
"I can not climb over the fence.
I will have to go under it."

The little pig worked and worked to get out.

Soon Mr. Pepper saw him.

"Stop, little pig!" he called.
"I will feed you."

Yes – No

Mr. Pepper had pigs on his farm.   _____

Baby rabbits lived on the farm.   _____

One pig looked for Mr. Pepper.   _____

The pig did not climb over the fence. _____

The hens had eggs for Mr. Pepper.   _____

Mr. Pepper saw the little pig.   _____

Mr. Pepper came to feed the pigs.   _____

Purpose: Comprehension—relevancy.
Directions: Read the title and the story. Then read each sentence below the story. If the sentence tells about the story, write *Yes*. If it does not, write *No*.
Use: With pages 82–87, *Around Green Hills*. **New Words:** *pigs, when, feed, fence, climb.*

Who Did It?

<u>Mrs. Wills</u> gave a party for Dick's friends.

Who gave the party?

Mrs. Wills rolled pretty eggs down a hill.

Who rolled the eggs?

The boys ran down the hill.

Who ran down the hill?

Jimmy and Jack looked here and there.

Who looked here and there?

But Freddie came back first.

Who came back first?

Freddie had all the eggs his hat would hold.

Who had many eggs?

Purpose: Comprehension—subjects of sentences.
Directions: Read the first sentence and the question about it. Draw a line under the part of the sentence that answers the question. The first one is done for you. Do the same with each sentence and question. Draw a line under just the part that answers the question.

42   **Use:** With pages 82–87, *Around Green Hills.*   **New Words:** None.

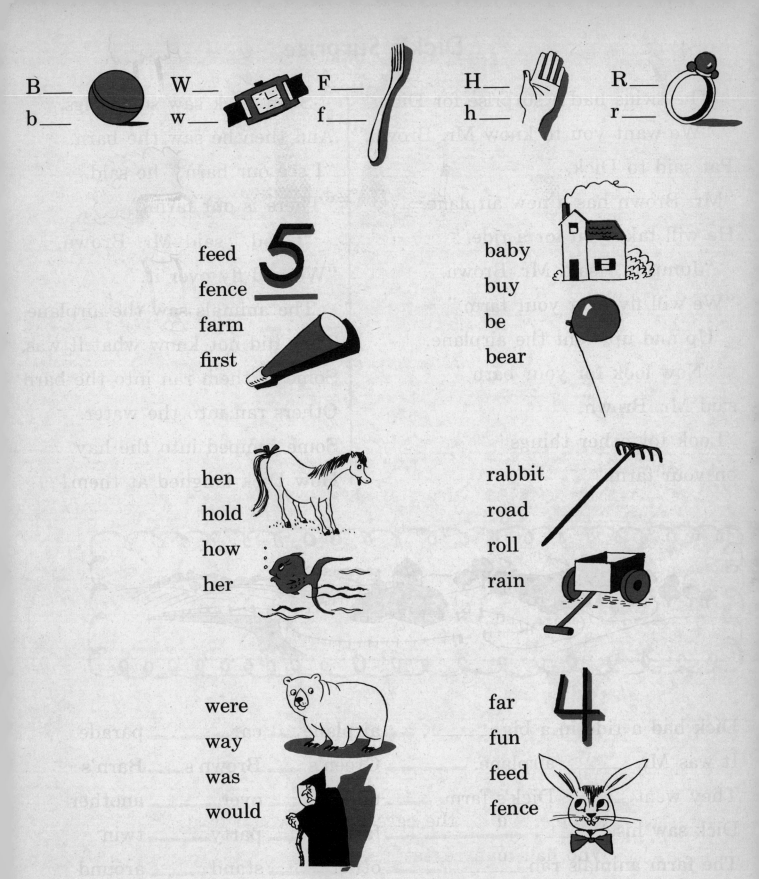

B ___
b ___

W ___
w ___

F ___
f ___

H ___
h ___

R ___
r ___

feed
fence
farm
first

baby
buy
be
bear

hen
hold
how
her

rabbit
road
roll
rain

were
way
was
would

far
fun
feed
fence

Purpose: Phonics—initial consonant letters and sounds.
Direction: Say the name of each key picture and listen to the sound of the first letter. Then say the words and the names of the pictures beside them. Draw a line under the picture beginning with the same sound as the words next to it.
Use: With pages 82–87, *Around Green Hills*. **New Words:** None.

Dick's Surprise

The twins had a surprise for Dick.

"We want you to know Mr. Brown,"
Pat said to Dick.

"Mr. Brown has a new airplane.
He will take you for a ride."

"Jump in," said Mr. Brown.
"We will fly over your farm."

Up and up went the airplane.

"Now look for your barn,"
said Mr. Brown.
"Look for other things
on your farm."

Soon Dick saw some pigs.

And then he saw the barn.

"I see our barn," he said.

"There is our farm."

"Good," said Mr. Brown.
"We will fly over it."

The animals saw the airplane.

They did not know what it was.

Some of them ran into the barn.

Others ran into the water.

Some jumped into the hay.

How Dick laughed at them!

Dick had a ride in a big _____ . ____ airplane ____ car _____ parade

It was Mr. _____ airplane. ____ Green's ____ Brown's ____ Barn's

They went _____ Dick's farm. ____ under ____ over ____ another

Dick saw his _____ . _____ farm ____ party ____ twin

The farm animals ran _____ . ____ other ____ stand ____ around

The _____ had a surprise, too. ____ airplane ____ Parkers ____ animals

Purpose: Comprehension—drawing conclusions.

Directions: Read the title and the story. Then read the sentences below and draw a line under the word at the right that belongs in each sentence.

44   **Use:** With pages 88–93, *Around Green Hills.*   **New Words:** *barn, other, some, water, hay.*

Dick's dog knows how to <u>roll</u> over.

He is <u>rolling</u> over.

Dick's dog <u>rolled</u> over.

Now he is <u>standing</u> up.

Pat is _____ off the fence.

fall   falling   falls

Dick _____ the fence.

climb   climbed   climbing

Mr. Wills is _____ Old Joe.

feeds   feed   feeding

Penny _____ a rabbit.

holds   hold   holding

Pat is _____ in some hay.

standing   stand   stands

Dick _____ the egg to Pat.

roll   rolling   rolled

Purpose: Phonics—verbs with *s, ed* and *ing* endings.
Directions: Study the key pictures and sentences with them. Study the underlined words and how they are used. Then read each sentence and the words under it. One of the words belongs in the sentence. Draw a line under the right word.
Use: With pages 88–93, *Around Green Hills.* **New Word:** *fall.*

45

day   call   hen   hat   down

may
way
hay

at
Pat
that

when
hen
then

brown
down
clown

fall
all
call

play
hay
way

Purpose: Phonics—rhymes (vowel-consonant blends).

Directions: Say the names of the key words and listen to the rhyming part that is underlined. Then say the words and the names of the pictures beside them. Draw a line under the picture that rhymes with the words next to it.

Use: With pages 88–93, *Around Green Hills.* **New Words:** None.

The Animal Party

The animals had a party.

"What can we do to have fun?"

asked the pig.

"I know something that is

a lot of fun," said the horse.

Then the horse said,

    "If I had some hay,

    I would eat all _____." _____ night _____ day _____ play

The rabbit said,

    "Can you tell me when

    We will see the _____?" _____ hen _____ then _____ egg

The pig said,

    "I have to be big,

    For I am a _____." _____ twin _____ pie _____ pig

The hen said,

    "I can eat a lot,

    But the duck can _____." _____ next _____ hold _____ not

The dog said,

    "The little pig came

    When I called his _____." _____ name _____ some _____ barn

Purpose: Phonics—rhymes.
Directions: Read the title and the first part of the story. Then read each unfinished rhyme and draw a line under the word that belongs in it. The right word rhymes and also makes sense in the sentence.
Use: With pages 94–95, *Around Green Hills*. **New Words:** *lot, if.*

car   <u>c</u>ar   <u>cold</u>

hold   h<u>old</u>

   It is a <u>cold</u> day.

bear   __ear   _____

look   l____

   Here is a story _____.

stand ___and   _____

hay   h___

   Sue, _____ where you are.

road   __oad   _____

fun   f___

   A horse can _____.

Purpose: Phonics—applying skills to new words from the next story: *cold, book, stay, run.*
Directions: Say the words *car* and *hold*.   Study the parts of words beside them and write the missing letters.
   Then use all the letters you wrote to make a new word in the box.   Write the word in the sentence below.
   Do the same with the other parts on the page.

48   **Use:** With pages 94–95, *Around Green Hills.*   **New Words:**   None.

Pat and Penny lived in this <u>old</u> house.

But now they live in a _____ one. ——— barn — hen — new

First the twins had to <u>work</u> for Mother.

Then they went out to _____ . ——— play — road — feed

In the <u>spring</u> Pat gave his old coat away.

But he will get a new coat in the _____ . — hay — fence — fall

Penny climbed up <u>on</u> Old Joe.

After the ride she had to get _____ . ——— if — off — some

Pat plays all <u>day</u>.

He does not play at _____ . ——— water — night — lot

Purpose: Comprehension—opposites.
Directions: Read the first pair of sentences. The first one has the word *old* underlined, and there is a word missing in the second. The word that belongs in the second is the opposite of the underlined word. Find it at the right and draw a line under the right word. Do the same with each pair of sentences.
Use: With pages 94–95, *Around Green Hills.* **New Words:** None.

49

Books and Names

Books have names
just like people and animals.
The name of this book
tells who is in the story.
Look at the name of the book.
Then draw a line under the animal
who is in the story.

Purpose: Comprehension—main idea, following directions.
Directions: Read the title and the story. Follow the directions given there. Draw a line under the animal or animals each book tells about.
Use: With pages 96–102, *Around Green Hills*. **New Word:** *books*.

Here is Sonny.

He is standing by his car.

Color Sonny yellow.

Color his car blue.

Here are Sonny's shoes.

He puts them on when he runs
from his story book.

Color Sonny's shoes brown.
Color the book red.

Here are things Sonny puts on
when he is cold.

Color the hat red
and the other things green.

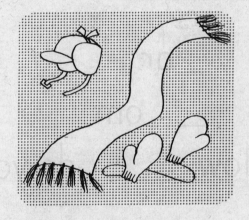

This is the little house where
the other ducks lived.
There is the water they played in.

Color the house yellow and
the water blue.

Purpose: Comprehension—following directions.
Directions: Read the directions and follow them.
Use: With pages 96–102, *Around Green Hills*. **New Words:** *Sonny, by, runs.*

51

cold   <u>c</u>old

climb   <u>cl</u>imb

Sonny did not like the <u>cold</u> water.

some   __ome

stay   ___ay

Here are _____ pretty books.

far   __ar

from   ___om

How ____ do you walk to school?

so   __o

stand   ___and

This bear is ___ old he can not run.

Purpose: Phonics—initial consonants (single sound and blends).

Directions: Say the words *cold* and *climb*. Study the parts of words beside them and write the missing letters. Then read the sentence and write the word that belongs in the sentence. Do the same with the other parts of the page.

Use: With pages 96–102, *Around Green Hills*.   **New Words:** *cold, stay*.

52

a _____   _____   _____

_____   _____   _____   _____

catch	if	when	stand	back	hen
a					
fish	that	them	went	pig	Dick

Best, get, yes, and **next** have the letter _____.

Him, wind, hill, and **twin** have the letter _____.

Had, hat, that, and **catch** have the letter _____.

Purpose: Phonics—short sounds of the vowels, *a, e,* and *i*.
Directions: Say the key words at the top and listen to the sounds of the first letters. Then say the name of each picture. If you hear the sound of *a* as in *at,* write *a.* If you hear the sound of *e* as in *egg,* write *e;* or *i* as in *it,* write *i.* Do the same with each word. Write the letter which stands for the sound you hear, *a, e,* or *i.* Write the letter that belongs in each sentence at the bottom of the page.
Use: With pages 103–108, *Around Green Hills.* **New Word:** *catch.*

53

Help for You

Ted did not want to <u>miss</u>
Jack's party. ___2___

Do you know <u>Miss</u> Barns? ___

1. Miss Parks

2. To miss
   something

Dick was the last boy
to catch a <u>fish</u>. ___

Ted could <u>fish</u> all day. ___

1. A fish

2. To fish
   in a brook

<u>Pat</u> and Penny are going
to the country to see Dick. ___

Sue likes to <u>pat</u> her dog. ___

1. Pat Green

2. To pat
   Old Joe's nose.

"<u>Stand</u> back of Polly,"
Penny said to Sue. ___

Dick made a <u>stand</u> at school. ___

1. A stand

2. To stand
   in water

Purpose: Comprehension—shifts of meaning.
Directions: Read the first pair of sentences and think of the different meanings of the underlined words.
Then study the pictures at the right. If the word *miss* in the first sentence means the same as picture 1,
write 1 on the line. If it means the same as picture 2, write 2. Follow the same directions for the rest
of the page.
Use: With pages 103–108, *Around Green Hills.* **New Words:** *last, could, fish, brook, country.*

fence _____	could _____	car _____	country _____ catch
feed _____	from _____	road _____	fence _____ farm
lot _____	rabbit _____	brook _____	rain _____ Sonny
water _____	hay _____	hold _____	when _____ some
from _____	dog _____	other _____	hen _____ how
barn _____	fall _____	by _____	stay _____ baby
road _____	rabbit _____	Dick _____	cold _____ hold
fence _____	fall _____	hen _____	another _____ climb
pig _____	feed _____	their _____	when _____ run
door _____	stay _____	road _____	other _____ could
catch _____	some _____	clown _____	name _____ farm
fish _____	climb _____	hold _____	if _____ last
would _____	their _____	night _____	another _____ animal
lot _____	last _____	next _____	just _____ book
water _____	yard _____	egg _____	could _____ hay
how _____	stand _____	country _____	hen _____ fall

Purpose: Phonics—word recognition (Test). See the Teacher's Guide—Short Form in this book for the additional use of this page as a test of initial consonant sounds.
Directions: Listen to the word the teacher says. Draw a line under the right one. Do the same for each row.
Use: With pages 103–108, *Around Green Hills.* **Review:** Unit III New Words.

Dick lives on a farm.

He has many animals.

Some of them have names.

Dick knows their names.

The animals are Dick's friends.

Dick has a lot of _____ .

　　barns　　farms　　animals

Dick's animals have _____ .

　　cars　　names　　books

Penny likes to ride the horse
at Dick's farm.

If Old Joe does not have

to work, she rides him.

Penny holds on when she rides.

She does not want to fall.

Old Joe is a _____ .

　　hen　　horse　　baby

Penny rides on Old Joe's _____ .

　　nose　　name　　back

The other day Pat walked

down by a country brook.

He said, "This is a pretty brook.

I would like to stay here

and fish all day."

Pat saw some _____ .

　　water　　flowers　　way

He would like to catch a _____ .

　　pig　　book　　fish

Mrs. Hen saw Mrs. Duck.

"Good morning," she called.

"Take a walk with me."

"No, thank you," said Mrs. Duck.

"I cannot go with you this morning.

I have to stay here on my eggs."

Mrs. Duck has eggs _____ her.

　　under　　over　　other

Soon she will have baby _____ .

　　pigs　　ducks　　hens

Purpose: Comprehension—drawing conclusions (Test).
Directions: Read the first story and the unfinished sentence below it. Then draw a line under the word that belongs in the sentence. Do the same with the second sentence. Then follow the same directions for each story on this page.
Use: With pages 103–108, *Around Green Hills*. **New Words:** None.

New Paint for the Fair

Pat went to see the people
get ready for the Fair.
He could not get in
to see them work.
But he could stand
by the green fence and look.

Pat could see a man
painting the rabbit house.
The man put a new coat
of yellow paint on the house.

Soon Pat ran to tell Penny
and his mother what he saw.

"The rabbit house is ready
for the Fair," said Pat.
"It is yellow now."

"The rabbit house
may be yellow," said Mother.
"But the fence is green."

"Yes it is," said Pat.
"But how do you know?"

"Look at your nose," said Penny.
"Just look at your nose!"

Pat looked.
His nose was green!

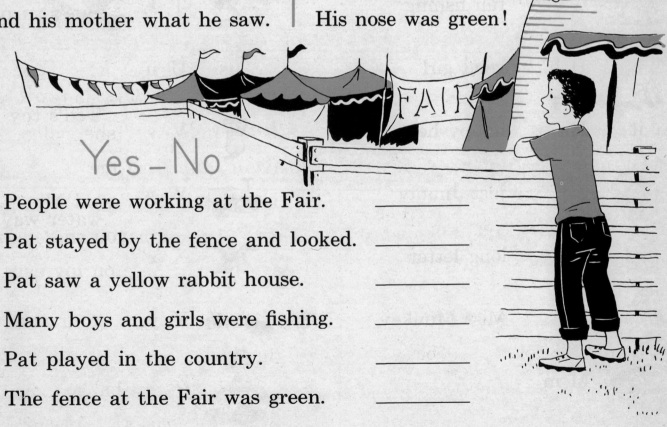

Yes — No

People were working at the Fair. _____

Pat stayed by the fence and looked. _____

Pat saw a yellow rabbit house. _____

Many boys and girls were fishing. _____

Pat played in the country. _____

The fence at the Fair was green. _____

Pat had green paint on his nose. _____

Purpose: Comprehension—relevancy.
Directions: Read the title and the story. Then read each sentence below the story. If the sentence tells about the story, write *Yes*. If it does not, write *No*.
Use: With pages 110–111, *Around Green Hills*. **New Words:** *fair, ready.*

57

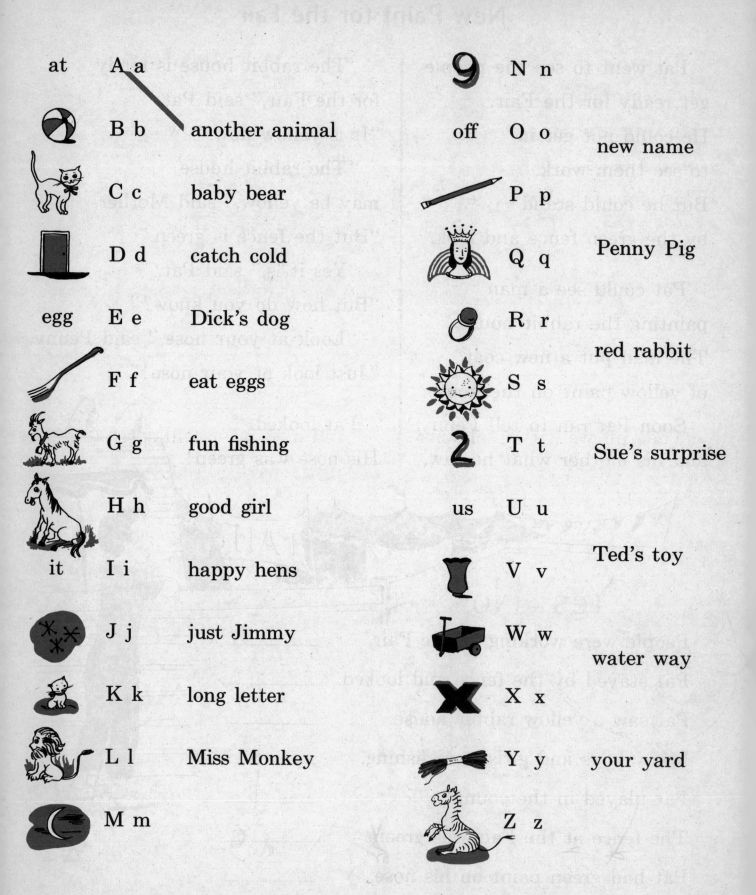

at	A a		9	N n	
	B b	another animal	off	O o	new name
	C c	baby bear		P p	
	D d	catch cold		Q q	Penny Pig
egg	E e	Dick's dog		R r	red rabbit
	F f	eat eggs		S s	
	G g	fun fishing	2	T t	Sue's surprise
	H h	good girl	us	U u	
it	I i	happy hens		V v	Ted's toy
	J j	just Jimmy		W w	water way
	K k	long letter		X x	
	L l	Miss Monkey		Y y	your yard
	M m			Z z	

Purpose: Phonics—first letters in ABC order.
Directions: Look at the pictures or words and the letters beside them. Then read each pair of words at the right. Decide what is the first letter of each word and draw a line from the right letter to that word.
Use: With pages 110–111, *Around Green Hills.* **New Words:** None.

58

The Balloon Parade

"Next week is the Fair,"
said a big balloon.
"And we are not ready
for the balloon parade.
This is a good day to get ready."

"Yes, it is a good day,"
said another balloon.
"We will not have time
to get ready next week.
We will get ready now."

Then off went the balloons.
What fun they had!

First came a red balloon
with a yellow nose.
Then came a yellow one
with a big red nose.

The next balloon was blue
with a little red nose.
The last one was green
with a brown nose.

"Now we are ready,"
said the first balloon.
"And next week will soon be here.
We will have fun at the Fair."

Purpose: Comprehension—sequence, following directions.
Directions: Read the title and the story. Then color each balloon as it is described in the story.
Use: With pages 110–111, *Around Green Hills*. New Word: *week*.

The Truck That Worked

Mr. Hays came to buy
a new truck for his farm.

"This truck is a good one,"
Mr. Weeks said to Mr. Hays.
"Many people saw it at the Fair.
The Fair Man said it was
a prize truck."

"Can it work fast?"
asked Mr. Hays.
"I want a truck that will help me
on my farm.
It will have lots of work to do."

"We will see," said Mr. Weeks.

The two of them climbed
into the new truck.
Away went the truck down the road
as fast as it could go.

Soon the truck came to the farm
where it went to work.
First it ran to the barn.
Then it went down the country road
and all around the farm.
It did a lot of work that morning.

At last Mr. Hays said,
"This is a prize truck.
I will buy it for my farm."

Who came to see Mr. Weeks? —————— Miss Parks — Mr. Hays — Mr. Wills

What did he want to buy? —————— a truck ——— a train ——— a duck

What did he want the truck to do? — work ————— fish ————— book

How many climbed into the truck? — one ————— two ————— three

What time of day was it? —————— night ——— morning ——— fast

Did Mr. Hays buy the truck? ————— Yes ————— No ————— By

Purpose: Comprehension—locating answers to questions, details.
Directions: Read the title and the story. Then read each question below the story. Find the answer at the right and draw a line under it.
Use: With pages 112–117, *Around Green Hills.* **New Words:** *truck, prize, fast, as.*

___ll

___st

___ck

___nd

___ng

___nt

best

fast

friend

fall

back

truck

long

spring

last

paint

Dick

want

went

tell

roll

wind

hill

stand

fast

just

thing

Purpose: Phonics—final consonant sounds (digraphs and blends).
Directions: Say the name of each key picture and listen to the last sound of each name. Then study the picture and words in each box. Draw a line under each word that ends with the same sound as the picture.
Use: With pages 112–117, *Around Green Hills.* **New Words:** None.

61

This egg is as big as the pumpkin.

The car is as long as the fence.

Yes   <u>No</u>

Yes   No

The big doll is as pretty
as the little doll.

Jimmy Parker can run as fast
as Jack White.

Yes   No

Yes   No

A pig is as big as a truck.

The doll is as big as Pepper.

Yes   No

Yes   No

The back wheel of this truck
is as big as the other wheel you see.

Polly's father is as old
as Mr. Little.

Yes   No

Yes   No

Purpose: Comprehension—drawing conclusions.
Directions: Read the first sentence and study the picture with it.   If the sentence is true, draw a line under
    Yes; if not, draw a line under *No.*   Do the same with each sentence on the page.
Use: With pages 112–117, *Around Green Hills.*   **New Words:** *pumpkin, wheel.*

62

Dick took a basket of apples
to the Fair.

The man at the Fair
looked at all the apples.
Then he said, "This basket
of apples gets first prize."

How happy Dick was to get
first prize for his apples!

Dick's apples were the best
at the Fair.

The apples had brown spots.

Freddie had a balloon.

"Do not let it go," said Jack.

But Freddie just laughed.

"My balloon will not get away
from me," he said.

Just then the wind came by.
It took the balloon up high,
over the trees and far away.

Freddie let the balloon go.

Jack helped Freddie catch
the balloon.

"Here is a monkey," said Jack.
"I have a penny for him."

"Where is your hat,
Little Monkey?" asked Polly.
"Jack has a penny for you."

The monkey took his hat
from under his coat.
Into the hat went the penny.

Jack gave the penny
to the monkey.

Polly took the penny.

Pat said, "My box of candy
has a prize in it."

"Let me see it," said Penny.

"All right," said Pat.
"Hold the box up high,
and you will find it."

Down on Penny's nose
came a little toy car.

There was no toy in the box.

The toy was under the candy
in the box.

Purpose: Comprehension—drawing conclusions.
Directions: Read the first story. Below it are two sentences. One sentence is true about the story and one
is not. Draw a line under the sentence that is true. Do the same with each story on this page.
Use: With pages 118–123, *Around Green Hills*. **New Words:** *took, spots, let, high, right.*

One Part — Two Parts

Fish __1__   Fishing __2__

Put **1** if there is one part.

Put **2** if there are two parts.

stay	1	catch	___	going	___
staying	2	catching	___	go	___
climbing	___	painting	___	walk	___
climb	___	paint	___	walking	___
fall	___	fishing	___	blowing	___
falling	___	fish	___	blow	___
buying	___	stand	___	feeding	___
buy	___	standing	___	feed	___

Purpose: Phonics—verbs with *ing* (hearing the extra syllable).
Directions: Say the word *fish* and then say *fishing*. You hear two parts in *fishing*. You hear *fish* and the sound of *ing*. Say each pair of words on the page. Follow the directions. If you hear one part, write 1; if you hear two parts, write 2.
Use: With pages 118–123, *Around Green Hills*. **New Words:** None.

64

"Look, Pat," said Penny.

"It is going to rain."

"It is raining now," said Pat.

"It rained all morning."

Freddie likes to _____ eggs.

color   coloring

Freddie is _____ one of the eggs.

eat   eating

Pepper is _____ in his house.

stayed   staying

Now Pepper is _____ over.

rolled   rolling

Ted has _____ a high tree.

climbed   climbing

Ted is _____ for apples.

looking   look

Purpose: Phonics—verbs with *ed* and *ing* endings.
Directions: Study the key pictures and sentences with them. Study the underlined words and see how they are used. Then read each sentence and the words below it. One of the words belongs in the sentence. Draw a line under the right word.
Use: With pages 118–123, *Around Green Hills.* **New Word:** *color.*

65

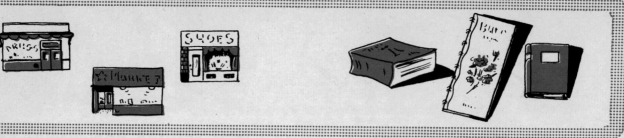

All are _____ .

<u>stores</u>   wheels   schools

All are _____ .

barns   books   brooks

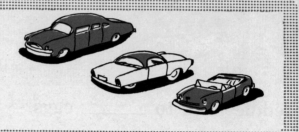

All are _____ .

towns   pumpkins   trucks

Parker   Green

Wills

All are _____ .

names   nights   barns

Dick Wills   Jack White

Pat Green

All are _____ .

stores   boys   girls

All are _____ .

yards   cars   coats

Freddie White   Penny Green

Sue Parker

All are _____ .

apples   children   twins

red   black

yellow

All are _____ .

colors   brooks   children

Purpose: Comprehension—classification.
Directions: Study the first picture and read the unfinished sentence under it. Find the word *stores* and draw a line under it. All the buildings in the picture are *stores*. Decide what all the pictures or words are and draw a line under the word that belongs in the sentence.
Use: With pages 124–128, *Around Green Hills*. **New Words:** *stores, towns, children, black.*

66

___o   ___ay   ___all   ___own

not <u>lot</u> spot town	way may stay book	___ook
all be call fall	took spot book brook	___ot
town so clown brown	hen then when cold	___en 10
cold hold old call	by my fly hen	___y
be she he stay	so by no go	___e

Purpose: Phonics—rhymes (vowels and vowel-consonant blends).
Directions: Use the key pictures to review the rhymes you know.   Then read the pair of words at the left of each box.   Find the word at the right that rhymes with those words.   Draw a line under it.   The first one is done for you.
Use: With pages 124–128, *Around Green Hills*.   **New Words:** None.

stay   st<u>ay</u>

store   st<u>ore</u>

Jack is in a toy <u>store</u> .

train   tr____

tree   tr___

He wants to buy a _____ .

black   bl____

blow   bl___

He wants a _____ train.

brook   br____

brown   br____

Jack does not want a _____ one.

Purpose: Phonics—vowels and vowel-consonant blends.

Directions: Say the words *stay* and *store*. Study the parts of words beside them and write the missing letters. Then read the sentence and write the word that belongs in the sentence. Do the same with the other parts of the page.

68   **Use:** With pages 124–128, *Around Green Hills*. **New Words:** None.

Fun for All

It was Halloween.

The mothers had a party
for all the children.

To the party came
a long Halloween parade.

There was a big white rabbit.

Back of him came two pigs
and a bear.

Then some clowns danced by.

Next came a little old woman.

She was a very little woman
with a very high hat.

"Name all of us!" she said.

The mothers took a long time.

At last they named all but two.

One was a very little man.

The other was a very big man.

"Show us who you are,"
said Mrs. Parker.

"No, we shall not,"
said the little man.

"Now I know," said Jimmy.

"Big Jack and little Freddie!
Show us who you are!"

"You are right, Jimmy,"
said Jack as he took off his hat.

Yes—No

There was a Halloween party.   _____

Children came to the party.   _____

The fathers gave the party.   _____

The mothers named some of the children. _____

Jimmy named the last two.   _____

The big man was Jack White.   _____

A little old man went fishing.   _____

Purpose: Comprehension—relevancy.
Directions: Read the title and the story. Then read each sentence below the story. If the sentence tells
about the story, write Yes. If it does not, write No.
Use: With pages 129–134, Around Green Hills.   New Words: Halloween, woman, very, show, shall.

 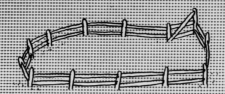 

Around this barn is a yard.   It is a barnyard.

On the farm is a house

where Dick Wills lives.

It is a _____ .

farmhouse   birdhouse   barnyard

There is a coat you put on

when you walk in the rain.

It is a _____ .

barnyard   raincoat   workman

At night the hen likes to go

into her house.

She runs to her _____ .

raincoat   doghouse   henhouse

In the spring you may see

a bird that is red.

It is a _____ .

farmhouse   redbird   blackbird

Purpose: Comprehension—compound words.
Directions: Read the two sentences and study the pictures at the top of the page.   Find the word *barnyard*.
It is made by putting the words *barn* and *yard* together.   Then read each unfinished sentence below.
Draw a line under the word that belongs in it.   The right word is made of the two smaller words that are
underlined.

70   **Use:** With pages 129–134, *Around Green Hills*.   **New Words:** None.

One Part —— Two Parts

Hen ___1___   Henhouse ___2___

Put **1** if there is one part.

Put **2** if there are two parts.

barn ___1___	man _____	blackbird _____
barnyard ___2___	workman _____	black _____
bluebird _____	school _____	dog _____
blue _____	schoolyard _____	doghouse _____
house _____	hen _____	farm _____
farmhouse _____	henhouse _____	farmhouse _____
raincoat _____	birdhouse _____	work _____
rain _____	bird _____	workman _____

Purpose: Phonics—compounds (hearing the syllables).
Directions: Say the word *hen* and then say *henhouse*. You hear two parts in *henhouse*. You hear the word *hen* and the word *house*. Say each pair of words on the page. Follow the directions. If you hear one part, write 1. If you hear two parts, write 2.
Use: With pages 129–134, *Around Green Hills*. **New Words:** None.

A Friend Finds a Home

Mr. Hillman had a good house to live in, but he was not happy. Many times he looked down the road and wished for a friend.

Late one night Mr. Hillman looked out from his doorway. A good spring rain began to fall.

Just then Mr. Hillman saw something coming down the road. Into the garden and up the walk came a funny black dog.

"Come in, Old Boy," Mr. Hillman called to the dog. "Stay here and be my friend. Make this house your home."

The dog did just that. He went in, and he stayed. Now Mr. Hillman is happy. He has a funny, old dog for a friend. And the good little house is their home.

What did Mr. Hillman want?	A friend	A show	A truck
What did Mr. Hillman see one night?	A car	A book	A dog
What color was the dog?	Black	Brown	Blue
Did he like the dog?	No	Yes	By
Did the dog stay with Mr. Hillman?	Yes	For a Day	No
Who is Mr. Hillman's friend?	Red Hen	Funny Pig	Old Boy

Purpose: Comprehension—locating answers to questions, details.
Directions: Read the title and the story. Then read each question below the story. Find the answer at the right and draw a line under it.
Use: With pages 135–140, *Around Green Hills.* **New Words:** *wished, late, began, funny, home.*

6   10

_i_   ___   ___   ___

___   ___   ___   ___

wish	black	let	catch	if	pig
_i_	___	___	___	___	___
as	hen	next	his	ran	get
___	___	___	___	___	___

Black, catch, back, and **Pat** all have the letter ____ .

Wish, fish, Dick, and **pig** all have the letter ____ .

Let, next, then, and **when** all have the letter ____ .

Purpose: Phonics—short sounds of *a, e* and *i*.
Directions: Say the key words at the top and listen to the sounds of the first letters.   Then say the names of the pictures.   If you hear the sound of *a* as in *at*, write *a*.   If you hear the sound of *e* as in *egg*, write *e;* or *i* in *it*, write *i*.   Do the same with each word.   Write the letter which stands for the sound you hear, *a, e,* or *i*.   Then write the letter that belongs in each sentence at the bottom of the page.
Use: With pages 135–140, *Around Green Hills*.   **New Words:** None.

best _____ prize _____ store _____ fair _____ farm

ran _____ from _____ ready _____ funny _____ wheel

wish _____ took _____ let _____ truck _____ week

prize _____ pumpkin _____ right _____ spot _____ pat

woman _____ wheel _____ very _____ where _____ wish

get _____ fish _____ fast _____ black _____ funny

help _____ home _____ high _____ shall _____ hay

roll _____ right _____ spot _____ prize _____ that

pumpkin _____ catch _____ color _____ children _____ high

town _____ spot _____ hen _____ time _____ late

wish _____ Halloween _____ week _____ woman _____ began

stay _____ shall _____ show _____ wheel _____ wish

your _____ very _____ ready _____ black _____ yellow

hat _____ horse _____ town _____ time _____ home

lot _____ fair _____ late _____ let _____ last

began _____ as _____ big _____ water _____ brook

Purpose: Phonics—word recognition (Test). See the Teacher's Guide—Short Form in this book for the additional use of this page as a test of vowel sounds.
Directions: Listen to the word the teacher says. Draw a line under the right one. Do the same for each row.
Use: With pages 135–140, *Around Green Hills*. **Review:** Unit IV New Words.

There was a very big pumpkin
in Freddie's garden.

"What a big pumpkin!"
said Freddie.

"It will be a good one
to show at the Fair."

Freddie has a big pumpkin.
He will take it to the Fair.
Freddie will buy a toy truck.

Penny was ready for Halloween!
She had on a high black hat.

"You look like the old woman
in the shoe," said Pat.

"She had so many children,
she did not know what to do."

Pat began to fall into the brook.
Penny was a little old woman.
Penny was ready for a party.

Polly called, "I am ready
for school, Jack."

"Ready for what?" said Jack.
"We do not go to school
this week."

Polly is ready for school.
Polly is late for the circus.
There is no school this week.

Jack took Freddie to the Fair.
Freddie began to look
at all the colors of the Fair.

He said, "I see so many colors.
There are as many colors
as I have in my paint box."

Jack took Freddie to the Fair.
Freddie saw many colors.
Three boys gave a funny show.

Purpose: Comprehension—relevancy (Test).
Directions: Read the first story and the three sentences below it. Two of the sentences tell about the story.
One does not. Draw a line under each sentence that tells about the story. Do the same with the other
stories on this page.
Use: With pages 135–140, *Around Green Hills*. **New Words:** None.

??How Many??

One cat   Two cats   Three cats

How many cats do you see here?   **Three**

How many cats are black?   **Two**

How many pumpkins do you see?   _____

How many pumpkins are happy?   _____

How many Halloween hats do you see?   _____

How many hats are high ones?   _____

How many children do you see?   _____

How many are over two years old?   _____

Purpose: Comprehension—definite terms.
Directions: Study the key pictures and labels at the top. Then study each picture below and read the pair of questions about it. Write the word that answers each question. The first one is done for you.
Use: With pages 141–143, *Around Green Hills.*   **New Words:** *cat, years.*

by   b_y

bat

cat   c_at

This Halloween _bat_ is flying.

far   __ar

_____

Pat   P___

Here is a _____ pumpkin.

may   __ay

_____

just   j____

The old woman _____ run fast

if she wants to catch the cat.

so   __o

_____

that   th___

The cat _____ on the fence all night.

Purpose: Phonics—applying skills to new words from the next story: _bat, fat, must, sat._
Directions: Say the words _by_ and _cat._ Study the parts of words beside them and write the missing letters.
   Then use all the letters you wrote to make a new word in the box. Write the word in the sentence below.
   Do the same with the other parts of the page.
Use: With pages 141–143, _Around Green Hills._ **New Words:** None.

77

The Fishing Cats
The Halloween Circus
Happy at Home

Bluebirds in the Barn
Halloween Fun
A Bear That Could Fly

A black cat said to his mother,
"This year I will have fun.
I am going to stay out late
on Halloween night."

But Halloween night was cold.
The wind was blowing in the trees,
and a cold rain was falling.
The cat was happy to stay home.

A little brown bat lived
in a barn with his mother.
"When can I fly out
with you?" asked the little bat.
"Halloween," said Mother Bat
At last Halloween came.
And off the bats went
for a night of fun.

Fat Little Bears
Baby Bears
Father Bear's Wish

The Pumpkin's Home
A Good Home
A Funny Cat

"Fall is here," said Mother Bear.
"There is no time to run about.
We must get ready
for the cold days that are coming.
We must eat and eat."

Soon the twin bears
were very, very fat.
They could not run about at all.

A little bird made a house
in a chimney.
"I will not be cold here,"
he said to the chimney.
"When the wind blows,
I will not know it.
I will be very happy here.
Thank you for my good home.'

Purpose: Comprehension—main idea.
Directions: Read the three titles and the first story. One of the titles goes with the story. Draw a line under the best title. Do the same for the other stories.
Use: With pages 144–149, *Around Green Hills.* **New Words:** *bat, fat, about, must, chimney.*

I am very fat.
But I am not a cat.

What am I?

chimney   bear   wheel

Here is something that I took
Out of the water in the brook.

What is it?

fish   year   first

The circus has come to town.
Look for me with a funny clown.

What am I?

country   morning   monkey

I sat with Father in this thing.
We went to town in the Spring.

What is it?

tree   chimney   truck

I am the animal
That may wish
To live in the water
Like a fish.

Who am I?

duck   cat   bat

I am big.
I am black.
I take boys about
High on my back.

Who am I?

prize   horse   color

Purpose: Comprehension—drawing conclusions.
Directions: Read the first riddle and the question below it. Decide which word is the right answer and draw
a line under it. Do the same with each riddle. Draw a line under the right answer.
Use: With pages 144–149, *Around Green Hills*. **New Word:** *sat.*

79

Draw lines under all the things you are to find.

Find two animals.

horse   black   dog   town

Find three people.

man   woman   clown   spot

Find two children.

Pat Chimney Country Penny

Find one woman.

Mr. Wills   Ted   Miss Parks

Find something cold.

show   last   fast   water

Find something high.

chimney ready baby dance

Find something that can roll.

sat   wheel   hay   week

Find something that can fly.

spot   barn   airplane   home

Find two things to climb.

fence   fall   tree   water

Find three things to buy.

pumpkin truck night book

Find something that must eat.

wish   fish   brook   funny

Find something that must blow.

late   color   wind   right

Purpose: Comprehension—indexing.
Directions: Follow the directions at the top of the page.
Use: With pages 144–149, *Around Green Hills*. New Words: None.

Help for You

Polly and Penny are going
to have a doll show.   __1__

Dick will show Pat
how to feed the pigs.   ___

1. A school show

2. To show
a new toy

"Oh me!" said Mrs. Little.
"I have broken my glass hen." ___

"Jack, please get me
a glass of water," said Polly. ___

1. A water glass

2. A glass fairy

Leaves do not fall
from the pine tree.   ___

"I must get a new coat
in the fall," said Mr. Day. ___

1. The fall
of the year

2. The leaves fall

No one wants to know a boy
who does not play fair.   ___

"Come on," called Freddie.
"We will be late for the Fair." ___

1. To play
fair

2. A Country
Fair

Purpose: Comprehension—shifts of meaning.
Directions: Read the first pair of sentences and think of the different meanings of the underlined words.
Then study the pictures at the right. If the word *show* in the first sentence means the same as picture 1,
write 1 on the line. If it means the same as picture 2, write 2. Follow the same directions for the rest
of the page.
Use: With pages 150–155, *Around Green Hills.* **New Words:** *broken, glass, fairy, pine, leaves.*

The Gold Fairy

A gold fairy was going to have
a party at her house.
She asked the animals to come.

She said, "I shall ask
the toy kitten, too."

"But the toy kitten is made
of glass," said the dog.
"She can not play with us."

"Just see," said the fairy.
Then she gave the glass kitten
a little pat.

The kitten began to dance.
But she danced around so fast
that down she went.

"Oh!" said the animals.
"The glass kitten is broken!
Good Fairy, what shall we do?"

"Just see," said the fairy.
Then she gave the broken kitten
another little pat.

Up jumped the glass kitten.
She was as good as new.

"What a good fairy you are!"
called the animals.

Then away they all ran
to the fairy's gold house.
And what a good time
they had at the party!

A _____ was going to have a party. _____ fair _____ funny _____ fairy

She asked _____ to come. _____ people _____ animals _____ children

She asked a _____ kitten to come, too. _____ glass _____ gold _____ pine

The kitten danced too _____ . _____ late _____ about _____ fast

The kitten was _____ . _____ brook _____ cold _____ broken

The _____ made her as good as new. _____ fairy _____ dog _____ bat

All the animals had a good _____ . _____ pine _____ time _____ fall

Purpose: Comprehension—details.
Directions: Read the title and the story. Then read the unfinished sentences below. Find the word at the right that belongs in the sentence and draw a line under it.
Use: With pages 150–155, *Around Green Hills.* **New Word:** *gold.*

gave   gave

hold   <u>h**old**</u>

gold

Here is a pretty <u>gold</u> fairy.

gold   _old

name   n____

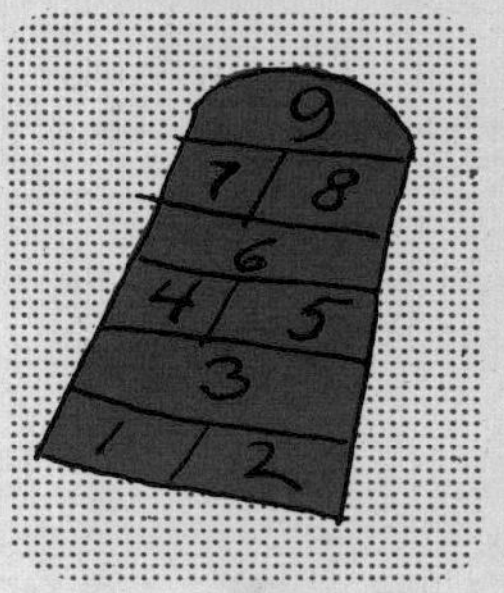

_ _ _ _ _

Do you play this _____?

green   __een

show   sh___

_ _ _ _ _

This kitten will _____
into a big black cat.

home   _ome

stand   st___

_ _ _ _ _

This doll has a broken _____

Purpose: Phonics—applying skills to new words from the next two stories: *game, grow, hand.*
Directions: Say the words *gave* and *hold.* Study the parts of words beside them and write the missing letters. Then use the letters you wrote to make a new word in the box and write the word in the sentence. Do the same with the other parts of the page.
Use: With pages 150–155, *Around Green Hills.* **New Words:** None.

83

Snow Fun

Freddie rolled around.

1. Who did something?

2. What did Freddie do?

Polly and Sue danced about.

1. Who did something?

2. What did the girls do?

Jack ran and jumped.

1. Who did something next?

2. What did Jack do?

Penny and Pat made a snowman.

1. Who made something?

2. What did the twins do?

Jimmy sat in a big old box.

1. Who did something?

2. What did Jimmy do?

Ted took Jimmy for a ride.

1. Then who did something?

2. What did Ted do?

Purpose: Comprehension—subjects and predicates of sentences.
Directions: Read the first sentence and question number 1. Draw one line under the part of the sentence that answers the question. Then read question number 2 and draw two lines under the part that answers that question. The first one is done for you. Do the same with each sentence and pair of questions on this page.

Use: With pages 156–161, *Around Green Hills*. **New Word:** *snow.*

This bird has made her home
in the pine tree.
The bird's home is in the tree.

The _____ bear ran away.　　This _____ has a flower on his head.

clown　　clown's　　　　　　clown　　clown's

Each _____ has a toy truck.　　This _____ truck is broken.

boy　　boy's　　　　　　　　boy's　　boy

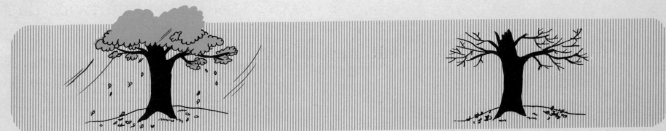

The _____ leaves are falling.　　Now the _____ has no leaves.

tree's　　tree　　　　　　　　tree　　tree's

Purpose: Phonics—nouns with *'s*.
Directions: Read the two sentences at the top and find the word *bird's*. The word *bird* with *'s* means the home belongs to the bird. Then read each sentence and the words below it. Draw a line under the word that belongs in each sentence.
Use: With pages 156–161, *Around Green Hills*.　**New Words:** *each, head*.

85

so   <u>s</u>o

snow   <u>sn</u>ow

Pat likes to play in the <u>snow</u>.

game   __ame

grow   ___ow

Pat and Dick play a _____
in the snow.

sat   __at

stay   ___ay

The boys would like to _____
out and play all day.

book   __ook

black   ___ack

Penny is in the farmhouse
looking at a good story _____.

Purpose: Phonics—initial consonants (single sounds and blends).
Directions: Say the words *so* and *snow*. Study the parts of words beside them and write the missing letters. Then read the sentence and write the word that belongs in the sentence. Do the same for the other parts of the page.
86   **Use:** With pages 156–161, *Around Green Hills*.   **New Words:** *game, grow*.

Mr. Green gave Pat a sled.

The sled was red and black.

It was very big.

"You can ride with me, Penny,"
said Pat.

"Let us go for a ride
right away."

The sled will hold _____ children.

many   two   no

Sue walked home from the store
with some apples and eggs.

One of the bags was broken,
and apples were rolling around.

"It is all right, Sue,"
said Mrs. Parker.

"The eggs are not broken."

The eggs were in _____ bag.

glass   broken   another

Mrs. White made a big cookie.

She made arms on the cookie.

She gave it two hands.

She put shoes on its feet
and a hat on its head.

At last the cookie was ready
for Freddie to see.

The cookie looked like a _____ .

boy   bat   bag

Freddie went out to play
with his new sled.

Soon his feet were cold.

His hands were cold, too.

"It is fun to play in the snow,"
said Freddie.

"But not when I am cold.

It is too cold for me in the yard.

I will not stay here."

Freddie will go into the _____ .

town   house   hand

Purpose: Comprehension—drawing conclusions.
Directions: Read the first story and the unfinished sentence below it. Draw a line under the word that belongs in the sentence. Do the same with each story on this page.
Use: With pages 162–167, *Around Green Hills*. **New Words:** *sled, cookie, arms, hands, feet, bags.*

at   egg   it

bag	sled	wish	pig	hand	let
a	___	___	___	___	___

hen	big	sat	next	fat	fish
___	___	___	___	___	___

a e i   Put the right letter in each one.   a e i

A b_i_g cat   A little f_sh   A b_g of apples

A green sl_d   A f_t pig   A mother h_n

Purpose: Phonics—vowel letters and sounds: *a, e, i.*
Directions: Use the key words at the top to review the sounds of *a, e,* and *i* in words. Then read each word and write the letter which stands for the sound you hear. Next, study each picture and write the missing letter. The word may be found in the top part of the page.

88 **Use:** With pages 162–167, *Around Green Hills.* **New Words:** None.

The Cookie Boy

Freddie wants a cookie boy.
Would you like to make one for him?

Put a head on the cookie boy.
Then put on a nose.

Next, make him so that
he can see.
He will want to eat, too.

The cookie boy must have
two arms and two hands.
Put arms and hands on him.

Next, he must have two feet.
Make a shoe for each of his feet.

Last of all, make a high hat
on the cookie boy's head.

Purpose: Comprehension—following directions.
Directions: Read the directions in the story and follow them.
Use: With pages 162–167, *Around Green Hills*. **New Words:** None.

The Little Old Clock

In a little old town there was
a little old house.
In the old house there was
a little old clock.

No one had lived in this house
for years.
And day after day the clock
just stayed by the door.

Now this old clock could talk.
Again and again he said,
"I wish I could run.
I wish my old wheels
would work again."

One day the clock saw a car
stop not far from the door.
"What do I see?" he asked.
Out of the car jumped a boy.
Then came another and another.
"Children!" said the old clock.
"They are coming here to live."
Then his wheels began to work.
"ONE and TWO and THREE,"
called the clock by the door.
At last the little old clock
in the little old house was happy.
He tells time night and day.

Yes - No

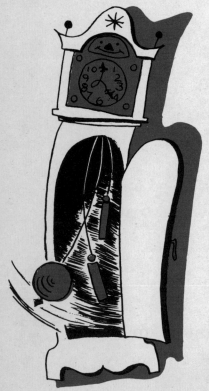

This story is about a talking clock. _____

This story is about a flying chimney. _____

The old clock wished to work again. _____

One day some children came in a car. _____

They came to live in the old house. _____

They came to find a fairy's store. _____

The wheels of the clock began to work. _____

Now the clock is happy. _____

He tells time for the children. _____

Purpose: Comprehension—relevancy.
Directions: Read the title and the story. Then read each sentence below the story. If it tells about the story, write *Yes*. If it does not, write *No*.
Use: With pages 168–173, *Around Green Hills*. **New Words:** *clock, talk, again.*

Can You Guess?

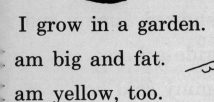

I grow in a garden.

I am big and fat.

I am yellow, too.

You can have fun with me
on Halloween.

Can you guess what I am?

    parade   pumpkin   chimney

My color is brown.

I look like a little boy.

I have feet but cannot walk.

I have a head but cannot talk.

I am very good to eat.

Can you guess what I am?

    country   pine   cookie

I am on your street.

I have many things to see.

Children come to me for candy.

Mothers come to buy apples
and eggs and other things.

Can you guess what I am?

    year   store   brook

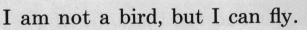

I am little and red.

I grow high on a tree.

Many boys like to climb
up the tree to get me.

Soon I may fall down.

Can you guess what I am?

    apple   sled   game

I am a little animal.

I live in a barn.

I am not a bird, but I can fly.

I fly around at night.

I am not very pretty.

Can you guess what I am?

    bat   horse   bag

I work for many people.

My wheels roll around
as I go up and down the streets.

I take things to stores.

I take things to homes.

Can you guess what I am?

    hands   clock   truck

Purpose: Comprehension—drawing conclusions.
Directions: Read the first riddle and the question below it. Decide which word is the right answer and draw
    a line under it. Do the same with each riddle on this page.
Use: With pages 168–173, *Around Green Hills.* **New Word:** *guess.*

91

The Parkers went away.
This story tells where they went.
Under the story you will see
a drawing that Sue made.
It shows the Parker car
about to leave the house.
Draw a line from the car
to show the roads it took.

First the car went to a big park.
Sue and Jimmy had fun there
looking at big brown bears.

Next, the car went to a big town.
Mrs. Parker had fun there, buying
lots of things in the big stores.

Then the car went over a brook
to a pretty farm in the country.
Mr. Parker showed Jimmy and
Sue how to ride a horse.

At last, Jimmy said he
would like to go home.

"How about seeing the circus?"
said his father.
"It is not far from here."

"No, thank you," said Jimmy.
"I just want to go home."

So back to Green Hills went
all the Parkers in their car.
And they were home that night.

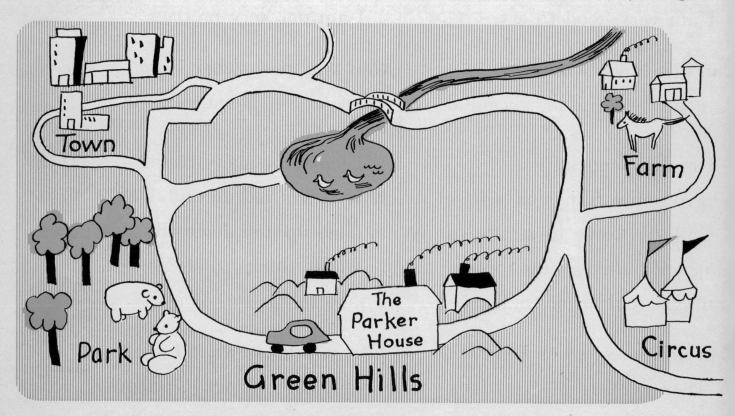

Purpose: Comprehension—following directions, sequence.
Directions: Read the directions and the story. Follow the directions by drawing a line on the roads the car traveled.
Use: With pages 174–179, *Around Green Hills.* **New Words:** None.

92

Green Hills Friends

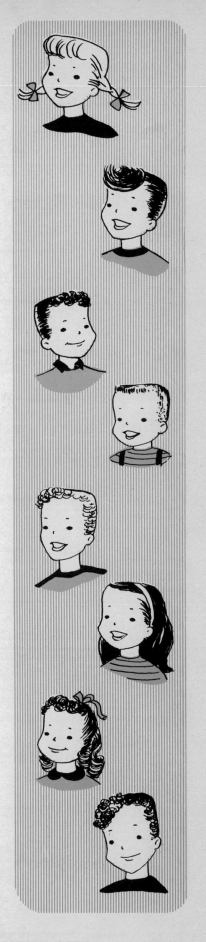

To _____, (Your name)

   We are the boys and girls
who live in Green Hills.
You can see us here.
And here are our names.
See if you can find
the right name for each of us.

   We would like to see you again.
We are happy that we know you.
We wish you many happy days
to come.

         Your friends,

Sue   Jimmy

   Pat   Ted

Jack Polly

         Penny

Freddie

Purpose: Comprehension—following directions.
Directions: Write your name on the line at the beginning of the letter. Then follow the directions in the letter.
Use: With pages 174–179, *Around Green Hills*. **New Words:** None.

93

ready —— each —— head —— hand —— fast

barn —— cookie —— brook —— broken —— woman

guess —— game —— late —— bag —— must

pine —— arm —— home —— by —— prize

fat —— town —— cat —— head —— feet

could —— spot —— shall —— sled —— sat

talk —— late —— town —— took —— black

grow —— ready —— year —— very —— week

bat —— fat —— fairy —— feet —— spot

country —— pumpkin —— cookie —— fairy —— chimney

right —— clock —— head —— leaves —— year

another —— each —— must —— after —— about

catch —— feed —— each —— eat —— leaves

brook —— grow —— snow —— glass —— gold

arms —— hands —— as —— game —— must

glass —— guess —— began —— again —— about

Purpose: Phonics—word recognition (Test).
Directions: Listen to the word the teacher says.   Draw a line under the right one.   Do the same for each row.
Use: With pages 174–179, *Around Green Hills.*   **Review:** Unit V New Words.

94

talk
==

| sled | toy | | feet | walk |

————————————————————

hand

| head | clock | | bag | stand |

————————————————————

grow

| pine | green | | snow | eat |

————————————————————

game

| good | late | | name | wish |

————————————————————

gold

| home | shall | | gave | hold |

————————————————————

sat

| town | soon | | fat | black |

————————————————————

must

| my | just | | spot | took |

Purpose: Phonics—identifying initial consonants and rhyming parts of words (Test).
Directions: Say the word *talk* and the words below it.   Draw one line under the word that begins like *talk*.
Draw two lines under the word that ends like, or rhymes with, *talk*.   Do the same with the rest of the
words on the page.   Find the two words that make the top word.
Use: With pages 174–179, *Around Green Hills*.   **New Words:** None.

Cold Days and Nights

The leaves are down.
This is a good time of year
for games in the snow.
Bats are put away,
but each boy has a sled.
He rides fast down the hill.

A fat man with a bag
comes down the chimney.
He talks to the pine tree
that he finds in the house.

"What pretty colors I see
on you," he calls.
"And I will put some toys
under you."

Colored leaves are on the tree.
The leaves are down.
Bats are put away.
It is the time for snow.
Boys ride sleds down the hill.
Flowers are in the garden.
A fat man puts toys under a tree.
Children will find toys there.

The Old Doll

A broken doll sat in her box.
She was not pretty.
Her head was broken, and she
had no arms and hands and fee
No little girl played with her.

The broken doll began to tall
"Help! Help!" she called.
"Please help me.
Do something
about my arms and feet.
Do something about my head."
A fairy saw the little doll.
"Be like new!" said the fairy.
And the doll was pretty again.

At first the doll was broken.
She had no hands.
Polly played with her.
This doll could talk.
She asked for help.
A fairy came to help the doll.
She could not help the doll.
Then the doll was pretty again.

Purpose: Comprehension—relevancy (Test).
Directions: Read the title and the story on the left. Then read each sentence below the story to see if it goes with the story. If it does, draw a line under the sentence. Do the same with the story on the right.
Use: With pages 174–179, *Around Green Hills*. **New Words:** None.